CONTENTS

I. I WANT TO BE . . . ?

"HULLO ! Commy. At last we've tracked you ! "

Four merry faces, very sunburnt, appeared over the screen of heather which I had fondly imagined was a safe retreat. Four accusing fingers pointed at me as Jill Wentworth said :

" Writing again ? Always writing ! I suppose writing isn't by any chance a *temptation* to you, Commy ? "

I closed up my pen with a guilty look.

" Sometimes—perhaps ! " I admitted. " But of course it *does* rather depend on the person to whom one is writing. At the moment, dear infants, I am penning a much overdue letter to my bank manager to ask for some more money. I only absented myself from your charming company because unless I get the money soon, Camp must starve."

A hollow groan escaped from Budge.

" Write on, Commy, write on ! " she implored. " I'll post the letter when it's finished."

" It is finished," I said. " But it seems a terrible thing that just because I come away with twenty girls I am never, from the moment I arrive till the moment I go, allowed to have a moment to myself."

" Commy ! " said Joan in a reproachful voice, " and you had ten whole minutes of your own company only this morning when we locked you in the bicycle shed."

" I was very busy then," I said. " If you want to know what I was busy with, you can all go and look at your front tyres when you get back to the Camp house."

" Commy ! You *didn't !* You *haven't !* " The four hurled themselves over the heather on to me. " I would never have believed you could be so revengeful," said Jill with a grin.

" It wasn't revenge, it was justice," I said. " What a set you are ! "

They were !—the most interesting set of all that interesting crowd of girls with whom I was on holiday in the hills of North Wales. Their names were Jill, Joan, Trim and Budge, and they were the merriest group in all that merry house-party.

It was a strange quartette in a way, for the girls were so different from each other. Jill was the most attractive in many ways. She was gay, quick and affectionate. Joan, her special friend, was a steadier girl, and she was a true Christian. She thought the world of Jill and had got her to Camp because of the help she hoped it might be to her friend. " Jill doesn't see things quite as I do," she confided to me one day, " but I don't think she's ever had the chance. She'll find it all at Camp because she's so real."

Trim, on the other hand, was an immensely precise person—hence her nickname. Her real name was Nancy Trimmel, but the girls had quickly discovered her passion for tidiness and accuracy, and had called her Trim. She was short and neat in her person, and she seldom spoke without thinking. She was a bit of a joke in the Camp, but Ma, our Camp Housemother, thought a lot of Trim—and Ma was a great judge of character.

Her friend Budge was an enigma to me. Betty Budgett was her name. She had been to two of my Camps and I couldn't think why. She said quite plainly that she didn't really like the Camp meetings, but that it was worth putting up with them for the sake of the games and outings She was an extraordinarily stubborn girl in many ways and I think that was why the girls nicknamed her Budge. Of course her name lent itself, as Trim's did, but it was a fact that once Betty Budgett had made up her mind, nothing seemed to move her.

Sometimes during our Camp talks in the evening I used to look at Budge and wonder sadly if she had made up her mind never to yield to Christ. She used to look so utterly unmoved—almost bored, at times. Yet she was never absent from any of the meetings. I think she felt it was the decent thing to take the pill with the jam, so to speak ! But there were times when I was very, very anxious about Budge, whom I liked immensely. Because, of course, I knew that nobody could go on indefinitely hearing the call and refusing to answer, without that call growing fainter with the passing years.

I think Trim and Budge thought a lot of Joan and Jill. At any rate the two pairs of chums were constantly together, and seemed to enjoy each other's company.

So I was not surprised when the quartette suddenly descended upon me when I was trying to find a few moments' quiet on the side of a heather-clad mountain.

" We've just been having a discussion among ourselves," said Joan.

" About vocation," said Trim solemnly.

" What a weighty subject for a hot afternoon," I laughed. " Are you going to drag me into it ? I'm not at all sure that my brain will stand it."

" Your brain will stand *anything*, Commy," Joan grinned. " Well, of course, Trim *would* give it a name like ' vocation,' but as a matter of fact, we were discussing what we wanted to do when we left school, and we were wondering if being a Christian made any difference to plans for the future."

I sat up.

" Ah ! now that *is* something worth talking about," I said, " and let me tell you straight away that it *does* make a difference and pretty big one."

I saw Budge glance up quickly. Then she said :

" How does it make a difference ? "

" In this way," I said, " that once you give your life to Christ, that life belongs to Him, and it is for *Him* to decide what shall be done with it."

I saw that Budge was prepared to offer a protest at this point, so I hurried on.

" In old days, when men kept slaves, the slaves left

it to their master to decide what they should do. All they did was to watch and listen for any direction the master gave them. Now St. Paul describes himself as ' the bond-slave of Jesus Christ,' and once we yield ourselves, soul and body, to our Lord, we too are His bond-slaves, and our job is to watch and listen for His direction."

Budge could contain herself no longer.

" But I should simply *hate* to be a bond-slave," she protested. " I'd far rather be free and able to choose for myself."

I looked at the others—at Trim, with her serious, contented face ; at Jill, who was looking at Budge with the concern she was unable to conceal ; at Joan, whose face was radiant. Joan answered my look with a quick smile, as she quoted : " ' Whose service is perfect freedom.' I'm so glad I'm a bond-slave now, Commy. But tell us, how are we to get His direction ? How does He show us the way ? "

" Ah ! now that's the next step," I said. " I think, Joan, that we receive guidance about our future in two ways, first by prayer and quiet waiting upon God, and secondly by the circumstances which God brings into our lives."

" Sounds suspiciously like a sermon with a firstly and secondly, Commy," Budge said.

" It does—and I believe it's going to be," I laughed. " But you can escape it, if you like, Budge. Never let it be said that anyone had to suffer my sermons unwillingly."

" No—she won't go. You just stay here," said Trim, putting a hand on her friend's arm. " Now go ahead, Commy."

" Well, as a matter of fact," I said, " I've started the sermon in the middle instead of at the beginning, but that was Joan's fault for asking the question. However —I'll carry on with the middle part and finish with the introduction.

" I am quite sure," I continued, " that—to carry on

the metaphor of the slave—just as the master tells the servant what he wishes him to do each day, so the Lord will tell us what is His will for us. Only it means that we must make time to listen to His voice. We can't expect Him to speak with us if we are too lazy, or too engaged with other things, to seek Him out and speak with Him. But if we do make this time, then He will clearly give us our orders, by bringing things to our remembrance."

" But we shan't actually hear a voice ? " Trim queried.

" No, probably not," I answered, " at any rate not a human voice. I think we shall hear a spiritual voice speaking to our spirits. But perhaps that is a bit hard to understand ? "

" No ; we know what you mean," said Joan. " There's a verse in Isaiah 30 you sometimes quote : ' *Thine ears shall hear a word behind thee saying, This is the way, walk ye in it.*' "

" That's just right, Joan," I said. " I've heard that voice often enough in my heart, during my quiet time, though anyone sitting in the same room would not have heard it."

" So have I," said Joan.

" And I," said Trim.

" Well, then, I think the other way in which God guides us about the future is by the circumstances in which He places us, and I do think we must be willing to be guided by these. I'll explain what I mean by a story."

" There was a girl whose great desire was to go abroad as a missionary. She really was so set on this particular form of service that she became entirely obsessed by it.

" When she was nineteen she decided to go to a missionary training college to prepare. She did not do well at it, and after a year's training, the Principal, who was a woman of rare and trained insight, advised her to seek some sphere of service in the homeland. She refused, saying that her heart was still set on going abroad.

"A year later, just as she was preparing to go, her father died suddenly, leaving her mother comparatively poor and and very delicate.

"There were no other children, and nobody in the family who could be called upon to help. There was not enough money to keep the mother in anything like the comfort that her health demanded. 'Now,' said everyone, 'this has at last shown Ellen that she is not meant to go abroad. She'll get a job at home and help her mother and make a much better thing of it.'

"But she didn't ! Ah yes ! "—as a distressed exclamation escaped from the listening girls—" Christians can be terribly selfish apart from the grace of God. She went abroad—her mother died within a year—and within another year that girl was back in the homeland, having lost her own faith and having helped to destroy the faith of many others."

"Is that a *true* story, Commy ? " asked Budge.

"Absolutely true ! " I replied. "My people knew the girl well. It goes to prove that we can only be shown His way if we are willing to see it in what He sends us. Some people you know, are apt to decide on their *own* way, label it *His* way and then get on with it. But now," I said, "for the introduction to the sermon, and it is this :

"This question which Trim calls 'vocation' is an immensely serious one for the Christian girl. She only has this one life to use for her Lord—only one chance to make a grand and beautiful thing of what He has entrusted to her. What does that little couplet say ?

'Only one life—'twill soon be past
Only what's done for Christ will last.'

"Mind you—*all* work *can* be done for Him, so long as it is the work He has chosen for you. It matters not whether it be missioning or charing—each is holy, if it be His choice, and done for His dear sake. Only we must be *dead certain* that it is what He wants us to do."

"Commy," said Joan, "there was an extraordinarily beautiful translation of some verse in one of the minor prophets that you gave us the other day which bears on this. Now what was it ? "

"Yes, I remember, Joan," I said. "It is a possible translation of Zephaniah 3 : 17, and it runs : '*He will silently plan for thee in love.*' That is so true for the Christian girl who is trusting her Father's love. She hasn't to fuss and worry about what the future holds. She has only to trust and to be guided, for her loving Lord is silently planning for her—in love. And if she will be willing, He will unfold the plan just at the right time and in the right way."

The Camp whistle blew from the valley beneath. Four serious faces looked up into mine, as they thanked me for the "sermon." I wondered, as we walked down the heathered slopes, what life held for each of them.

II. TALL, DARK AND HANDSOME

"Budge is on the warpath, Commy," said Joan, as I entered their dormitory one night just before the last bell was due to be rung.

"Budge is seldom off it," I said. "What is the line of attack to-night?"

"Well—it's arising out of what you said about vocation the other afternoon," said Budge. Then, much as a shot is fired from a pistol, she asked:

"Do you think it's wrong to want to get married?"

"No! of course I don't," I said. "I suppose I shouldn't be getting married myself next year if I did."

"Ah! but *you* want to marry one special person," said Budge.

"Well, my dear girl, how many do *you* want to marry?" I asked.

"Oh *Commy*! be quiet! You know that isn't what I mean. What I mean is—I don't want to be anything in particular, only I'd like to get married."

"Why?" I asked.

Budge seemed rather vague as to the exact reason, but I pressed her and at last she admitted.

"I should simply *hate* to be an old maid."

"But would you be?" I asked. "It seems to me that there are so few of them nowadays. It's true I do sometimes meet unmarried women who have grown selfish and self-centred through having nobody dependent on them, but in the main they all seem to be doing jobs and finding life very thrilling."

"Are they?" Budge asked dubiously. "I'd rather not risk it."

The others gave vent to a roar of laughter, which brought Ma to the door.

"Commy!" she said in mock reproving tones, "I

came to see what all this noise was about at nine-thirty in the evening."

" And I'm glad you *have* come, Ma," I said, " for Budge has got me out of my depth this time and I think I'll ask you to take over."

Ma's real name was Mrs. Marshall. We had come to call her Ma for two reasons. One was the obvious, because she was house-mother. The other was because at the first Camp, girls' voices were always to be heard calling, " Mrs. *Mar* . . . shall, Mrs. *Mar* . . . shall." So it quickly got shortened to " Ma " and Ma she has been ever since and always will be to the Campers.

" Getting out of your depth seems to amuse you all," laughed Ma. " Do you know that the last bell will go in less than a quarter of an hour and none of you is even undressed ? "

" But, Ma," I said, " there is far more important business on hand than undressing. Budge wishes to know if it is wrong to want to get married simply to escape being an old maid."

" Why, of course it is ! " said Ma promptly ; " it's silly, too, for it often means going out of the frying pan into the fire. I've been married ten years," she said, " and I married the right man. But I can tell you this that I would *infinitely* rather have stayed single for life than have married the wrong one."

" *Really ?* " said Budge.

" *Truly !* " answered Ma, " and I'm not saying that from the secure vantage post of being safely married. You know, what you girls seldom realise—and how can you be expected to ?—is that it's one thing to meet a man at parties and go out with him to tennis every so often, and it's an entirely different thing to sit opposite to him at breakfast for forty or fifty years without a break.

" You see," Ma went on, " if you, Budge, marry a man only for the sake of being married, after a year or two even the fact of being married won't console you for the frightfulness of having to look at him so often. Whereas, of course, if you marry him because you love him, and he is the one and only man in all the world for you, then the moments that you spend with him become increasingly precious as the years pass. That's the situation as I see it, and I ought to know," said Ma, sitting down on the edge of a bed.

"Well—I don't want to get married in quite the same way as Budge does," said Joan, "but at the same time I'd like it awfully if, as you say, Ma, I found the right man. I think the best thing to do is to take up some job in life, then if you get married well and good, and if you don't there is still the work to carry on with."

"That's what I think, Joan," said Ma. "And as a matter of fact, the things a girl learns while training are invaluable to her when it comes to walking in double harness. For, you know, if a home is to be truly happy there has got to be lots of unselfishness and yielding ; lots of sharing and being able to work together. When children come there must be endless patience and under-standing sympathy on the part of the mother or the home becomes like a ruffled hen-coop. I may also say," she continued, "that there must be a reasonably competent brain in the mother's head, or the home will not be as happy as it might, and the husband will get harassed. Oh, it's not a light job by any means, my dears ! "

"But you've made it sound a bit heavier than you need, haven't you, Ma ? " Budge protested.

"No ! I haven't," said Ma emphatically. "I haven't made it sound nearly as heavy as it can be. Add to all I've said the children having whooping cough ; the maid walking out at a moment's notice ; the butcher not delivering the steak ; the income tax man sending in the final demand ; the cakes getting burnt ; the washing line breaking on a muddy day ; the baby falling out of his perambulator and the husband losing his stud ; and you've got the picture."

"Oh Ma ! " I clapped my hands over my ears, while

the girls rocked with laughter. " For pity's sake stop, or I shall be breaking off my engagement."

" Not you ! " said Ma with a side glance in my direction. " If I went on all night *you* wouldn't. Yours is one of the ones that are made in heaven. But seriously," she added, turning to the girls, " I have said all this because Budge, and many, many girls like her, have *no* idea whatever of what marriage brings. They look at it simply in the glowing colours of their engagement ring, and if only they would *think* they would not rush into it so lightheartedly ' just for the sake of being married.' "

Suddenly Budge looked very serious.

" I say—thank you, Ma ! " she said ; " I certainly hadn't thought. If I'm ever tempted to marry for the sake of being married I'll remember the whooping cough, and the butcher and the maid and the income tax and —oh yes, most of all I'll remember the fifty years of breakfasts and the husband's stud ! "

" I know what you've said is true, Ma," I said, " for only yesterday I had this letter from a friend of mine who married a year ago, and went to Australia. Let me just read you this bit."

I pulled a letter out of my pocket and read :

" ' We are very happy, for we know now that our love for each other will deepen and increase with every year that passes. But I had no idea whatever of what the everyday details of married life would entail, or of the endless intimacy of married life. It is all so beautiful when the love is as real as ours is, but I shudder to think of the irksomeness of it all without such love. I wish I could tell every unmarried girl I know of what is in store for her, and beg her not to rush into it carelessly and without thought.' "

" Then how can we know if it is the right person ? " Jill asked.

"Well," said Ma, "I believe in the old-fashioned idea of falling in love. I believe there is something within you which glows and leaps into life when you meet your mate, and you know it. I don't say it necessarily happens the first time you meet, but I'm sure it does at some time in your contact with him. And unless that love is there it is a poor outlook for the future.

"Why," she continued, "I knew two young people some years ago and they fell in love with each other. What he could possibly see in her I could not imagine. He was tall and kind and good looking, but she would have made a good wife for a blind man—she was just about the plainest girl I've ever seen. Also, I didn't think she was a very attractive nature—she could be very snappy at times. But they just adored each other. Sometimes people said to me, ' That's an ill-matched couple. He'll get tired of her.' But I knew he wouldn't. He really loved her.

"They have been married some time now, and they have three children all as plain as their mother. I went to stay with them just before I came to Camp, and really, their devotion almost made me weep, it was so lovely. That handsome man sat beside me on the lawn and watched his wife and children with a look of infinite tenderness and pride.

" ' Aren't they a quartette to be proud of?' he asked.

"And, suddenly, seeing them through his eyes, I found I could answer quite honestly, ' Yes ! they are.'

"For I noticed that the wife's face had lost its temperish look and had acquired a rather sweet contentment. And the children, products of a peaceful, happy home, had pleasant expressions, if plain features. And it was all because love was there.

"Ah yes," Ma concluded, "if the love is real then it triumphs over everything—even whooping cough, income tax, the butcher and all the rest of it. But if the love isn't real, it sinks under it."

There was silence in the dormitory for a few minutes

after that. We were all thinking pretty deeply. Trim broke the silence by saying :

"I suppose, Ma, if you're a Christian you can't marry a man who isn't ? "

Ma's face was very serious as she replied :

"No, Trim, I'm afraid you dare not ! It's put so clearly in the Guide Book. '*Be not unequally yoked together with unbelievers.*' '*Can two walk together unless they be agreed ?*' Of course they can't—especially in the closest walk of all."

There was a look of quiet trust on Joan's face as she said :

"But I suppose it just is that if we let God choose for us, He chooses the best, and sees that we lack nothing ? "

"That's it, Joan," I said.

> '*He knows ; He loves ; He cares ;*
> *Nothing this truth can dim.*
> *He gives the very best to those*
> *Who leave the choice with Him.*' "

The "lights out" bell rang through the house. Ma, with a chuckle, went to the door and switched off the light.

"You are fortunate," she said, "you've at least got the moon to undress by. Good night all of you ! Good night ! "

III. JILL IS IN EARNEST

"I SAY, Commy, are you off for an evening stroll?"

Jill Wentworth's merry face appeared out of one of the windows of the Camp house, as I turned a corner of the drive.

"I am," I said. "As a matter of fact, my dear Jill, I am by way of seeking a little rest from the clatter and chatter of twenty schoolgirls."

"Then may I come and seek it with you, Commy?"

"*You!*" I retorted. "Why! you're the most clattering and chattering of them all!"

"That's true!" she replied. "All right, Commy! I'll be with you in half a minute."

She was, and we walked side by side through the garden and out into the road.

"Now which way?" she asked.

"Up through the Cader Glen," I said. "There's a lovely view of the sea and the distant hills when you get to the end of it and we've plenty of time to do it and be back by bedtime. I did this walk with Ma yesterday. By the way, why aren't you playing tennis with the others?" I asked.

"Because I wanted to talk to you," said Jill.

"I'm flattered!" I said. "Now," as we entered the damp, leafy shade of the glen, "have you ever seen anything prettier than this?"

"No! I don't think I have," was the reply. The stream burbled between high banks, soft with ferns and flowers, and over great boulders green and grey with moss and lichen. The setting sun, caught in the splash of the water, made myriad rainbow-coloured drops, until it looked as though a shower of gems was being dropped by careless hands into the passing water.

"My!" said Jill appreciatively, as we reached the

end of the glen, " it's lovely ! I *am* enjoying this Camp,
Commy. When Joan asked me to come, I thought that
it would be frightfully stuffy, but it's not."

" Now that's something to be really thankful for,"
I said, solemnly. " But why stuffy, Jill ? We keep all
the windows open."

Jill grinned.

" Yes, but a Camp in a house seemed awfully weak
after being under canvas, and besides, I thought it would
all be Bible-reading and hymn-singing and that sort of
thing."

" Well—there *is* quite a lot of that," I said.

" Yes ! " Jill admitted, " but somehow it's not what I
thought it would be like. I say, Commy, I asked to
come with you to-night because, because . . ." Her
voice broke slightly. " I'm in dead earnest."

We had come out into the open by this time, and the
sea spread like a vast, unruffled mirror before us. Away
to the far distances the Welsh mountains softly rose and
fell with here and there a sudden, sharp peak rising out
of the rounded summits. The sun was sinking slowly
behind silver and purple clouds, and there was no sound
in all the vast space around us, save our own voices and
the occasional lonely cry of a sea-bird on the wing.

I gave one glance at the girl's face and knew that she
spoke the truth.

" Then let's sit here," I said, pointing to a tufty hum-
mock of grass, " and tell me, Jill, what are you in earnest
about ? "

" Life ! " said the girl, briefly—" and after."

We sat quietly for a few moments after that. She was
struggling for words, and I was praying for wisdom. It
was Jill who spoke first and her words came rapidly and
sincerely.

" You see, it's like this, Commy. Joan and I have
been awfully good pals for two years now—ever since we
were in the fourth together. I've always admired her
tremendously—more than any other girl. It's not only

that she's dead straight, and good at games—it's just something about her that is somehow *above* all the rest of us, if you understand what I mean ? "

I nodded. I did understand, for I knew Joan.

" Well," Jill went on, " I really only came to Camp because I liked her so, and she kept pressing me to come, not because I wanted to be different in myself."

I nodded again. I had known that, too.

" But now," said Jill, looking up with puzzled, anxious eyes, " I *do* want to be different. Why is it, Commy ? "

" It is because, for the first time, you have met Christ and realised something of His claim upon you," I said.

" Ye—es ! that's true," was the thoughtful reply. " But, Commy, *why* have I felt it ? *Why* has He this claim upon me ? "

" Jill," I said quietly, " are you a sinner ? "

She looked up with a startled glance.

" Well," I said, when no reply was forthcoming. " Let me put it another way. Have you ever sinned ? "

" Oh yes ! " was the ready answer. " Often ! "

" Then," I repeated, " are you a sinner ? "

" Yes, I suppose I am ! Of course I am ! Somehow it sounds worse to be a sinner than just to have sinned. But I suppose that if I've *done* the one, I *am* the other."

" Exactly ! The Bible puts it for us clearly enough. ' *Whosoever shall keep the whole law and yet offend in one point, he is guilty of all.*' ' *All have sinned and come short of the glory of God.*' Well now, Jill, what you've never realised till now is that something had to be done about sin."

" Yes ? "

" And it was what the Lord Jesus Christ did about it that has constituted His claim upon you. Let me tell you something that a little child whom I knew once said when she was three years old."

Jill settled herself more comfortably on the grassy tuft. She liked a story.

" It happened when this little girl was being tucked

up in bed one Saturday night. The day had been rather a great occasion, for she had received her first pocket money. One penny seemed a vast sum, and all the morning, as she had gone through the village, she had been asking, ' How much does that cost, Mummy ? Does that blue trike cost a penny ? Is that ball a penny ? Does a doll's house cost a penny ? '

" And now the evening had come and she had sung ' *There is a green hill*,' and she had said her prayers, and her mother was just leaving the room when the little girl recalled her.

" ' Mummy ! ' she said, ' How much does sin cost ? ' "

" Her mother thought of the penny pocket money and barely restrained a smile.

" ' Well—you can't buy sin, darling,' she said. ' Sin is a horrid——'

" ' Oh yes, you can, Mummy ! ' the little girl interrupted eagerly. ' My hymn said you could.'

" ' Your hymn said you could ! Where does it say that ? ' asked the mother.

" ' It says :

> *There was no other good enough*
> *To pay the price of sin.*

and I want to know, Mummy, how much did sin cost Lord Jesus ? ' "

I ceased talking for a moment. The girl beside me was looking thoughtfully out to sea.

" Jill, you *are* a sinner," I said. " You have just told me so, and I am glad indeed that you know it, for until you know it you can never get any further. Now, my dear girl, do you know what that sin of yours cost the Son of God ? "

" I think I know—now," was the reply.

" It cost Him His life," I said. " It cost Him all the glory of Heaven—all the loneliness of earth. It cost Him all He had—save His Deity—in order that you, Jill, might be saved from the awful consequences of your sin. '*The Son of God . . . loved me and gave Himself for me.*' That is His claim upon you. Just that ! "

There was silence again, for quite a long time. Then Jill asked :

" And in return He asks from me ? "

" *Your* heart—*your* life," I finished. " Just you yourself given to Him because He gave Himself for you."

" That's fair ! That's right," said Jill. " Commy—let's pray."

Together we knelt on the hillside and Jill prayed. As she did so, the sun sank, and when we rose from our knees the darkness had almost descended on us. But there was a light in the eyes of the girl beside me such as I had never seen on her face before, and as she gripped my hand she whispered :

" Commy ! it's happened ! I'm different ! I belong to Jesus Christ."

"Commy ! Shall I always feel as happy as I do now ? "

I had not seen Jill alone since the evening we had walked together through the Cader Glen, but I had watched with joy the difference in her. She had always been a gay, laughing person, generally with a crowd round her, but during the past week there had been a different quality about her laughter and a more joyous light in her eyes. I had seen Budge looking curiously at her once or twice.

So now I welcomed the opportunity of a chat with her. Most of the girls were scattered round the garden, writing letters. I had just finished mine when Jill accosted me with her question. She was not given to wasting time over preliminaries.

" I can think better walking," I said, " or throwing stones into the sea. Let's go down to the beach. The night is yet young."

We slipped out of the little garden gate which opened into a narrow lane leading to the sea. In three minutes we were on the beach, the sea lapping at our feet.

" The shore is very deserted to-night," I said, " and I believe there's a storm brewing." Great purple clouds were gathering on the horizon. It was the first sign of bad weather since Camp started. " But now," I said, " for your question—No ! I don't think you will always feel as happy as you do now."

" I don't mean on account of circumstances," said Jill. " I know that things will go wrong at times, and we're all bound to have trouble at some time or another. Christians aren't exempt from that, are they, Commy ? "

" No ! indeed they are not," I said. " In fact often it is our Lord's way of bringing great blessing to our souls. ' *Whom the Lord loveth, He chasteneth*,' and when these troublous times come to the Christian girl, she must

hang on to the fact that ' *all things work together for good
to them that love God.*' That's been a wonderful help to
me sometimes when I haven't been able to understand
the way He was leading me."

"That's a grand text," said Jill. "Just before we go
on to what I'm really getting at, tell me where it's found,
Commy."

"Romans 8 : 28," I said. "Mark it in your Bible
and keep it in your heart, Jill. It's for the times when
things don't work out as you want them to. I must just
tell you about one time last year when I hung on to it.
One of my uncles—I'm his god-child—had planned a
perfectly glorious cruise—and he was going to take me
with him. You can imagine what I felt like ! We
were going to India, and then on to China, and it was
going to take three months. I was nearly crazy with
excitement. Then, the very week we were due to start,
when all my boxes were packed and I was going round
saying good-bye to my friends, there came a telephone
message to say that uncle had been taken suddenly ill
and the trip was off. I took that message, and my
disappointment nearly choked me. It was all I could
do to find voice enough to send him my love and say how
sorry I was. I simply couldn't tell Mother, who was in
the next room. I remember rushing upstairs to my
bedroom, locking the door and saying, over and over
again, "all things work together for good . . . all
things work together for good." I couldn't think of
anything else to say.

"Well—everybody was terribly nice about it, but
that didn't alter the fact that I had to unpack my boxes
and plan another holiday. All my friends had fixed
theirs up, and the only thing left to me was to go for a
fortnight to an exceedingly dull place on the South Coast
with an exceedingly dull aunt. I would much rather
have stayed at home, but my people very much wanted
me to go, so I had to. And all the time I kept holding
on to Romans 8 : 28.

" The first week of that holiday was even duller than I had expected. But—you see—the second week I met the man I'm going to marry. And, Jill, I'm so *glad* I trusted my Lord through that disappointment, and didn't rebel. He had something better in store. But now I've wandered off your track a bit."

" My ! but I'm glad you did," said Jill, with shining eyes. " I'll never forget that story, or the text, Commy. These disappointments are bound to come to me. I'll just hold on to that verse.

" But what I was really getting at was this," she said. " I've felt so absolutely happy—so perfectly sure about everything—this last week. Does that last, Commy ? "

" It can," I said, " but I must tell you, Jill, it sometimes doesn't."

" Why not ? "

" Because your adversary, the devil, as a roaring lion, walketh about seeking whom he may devour," I said.

" You mean that the devil will make it his business to try to wreck my faith ? "

" Yes ! just that ! He will come to you one morning when you feel ' down ' and when something has gone wrong, and he will say to you, ' Where is your joy now ? What was the good of trusting Christ ? It was only the excitement of Camp. Your Lord has let you down already.' "

" And when he does that, Commy ? "

" Then, Jill, take your Bible in your hands and say to him, ' *I* know *whom I have believed, and am persuaded that He is able to keep that which I have committed unto Him.*' What have you committed unto Him ? " I asked.

" Well—everything," was the reply. " My heart and my life and—everything."

" Then it's that which He is able to keep—just what you've committed to Him," I said.

" Yes ! I see ! " said Jill, thoughtfully. " I must make a note of that verse, too, Commy. Where is it ? "

" II Timothy 1 : 12," I replied. " But, of course, the

devil will not give you up in a hurry," I continued. " We
need to remember that he is a persistent foe, and it hinders
his work a lot when he finds a real, trusting, Christian
girl, so he does all he can, especially while she is young,
to try to wreck her faith. I remember very well what one
of his favourite lines of attack on me used to be, when I
first came to Christ."

" Tell me," said Jill.

" If I had fallen and done something which I knew had
displeased my Lord, he used to come and say,

" ' *Now* look what a fine Christian you are. You
might as well not be one for the way you behave. I
don't suppose you *are* one really—it was only just the
thrill of that meeting. Look at you, sinning just the
same. . . . ' "

" And then ? "

" Jill," I said, " what are you resting on—what are
you trusting in—for salvation ? "

The girl's eyes were thoughtful as she replied,

" I'm trusting in the Lord Jesus, Commy. I'm trusting
in His work on Calvary to cover my sin."

" Aren't you trusting in anything you've done ? "

" No ! I can't, can I ? I . . . I've been a sinner."

" Aren't you trusting in your decision the other night
—the decision you made to follow Christ ? "

Jill thought for quite a long time. Then :

" No ! " she said quietly. " I'm not trusting in that,
either, Commy. That was the sort of clinching of it,
if you see what I mean."

" Yes ! I see," I said. " So literally all you are
trusting in to be His child here and in heaven is—— ? "

" Him ! " said Jill.

" And can He change ? " I asked.

" No ! never ! " she said. " What was that verse
you gave us last night, Commy ? ' *Jesus Christ, the
same yesterday, and to-day, and for ever.* ' "

" And can His work on Calvary ever change, or be
undone ? " I asked.

" No ! never ! " was the emphatic reply. " He died, once for all."

" Then," I said, " you have for ever got your answer when the devil tempts you to feel you are not really Christ's. Say to him, ' But I *am—still*. I *must* be, for my salvation depends on *Him*, not me ; on *His* finished work, not on my trying—and failing. I'm trusting Him, not myself, and He never changes.'

" And then, Jill, into your heart there will come, as you kneel before your Lord, the sweet peace of forgiveness and assurance, and the quiet beauty of calm after a storm."

" Like that ! " said Jill, pointing to the western sky. I followed her glance and saw that where, before, the threatening clouds had gathered, there was now the calm and golden radiance of the setting sun.

" Yes ! " I said, " like that."

W_E had hired two boats and were out rowing. Ma was in one with five campers and I was in the other with Jill, Joan, Trim and Budge. For a time we kept together, then the others, who were stronger rowers than we were, sped past us round a headland and we were left to meander along at the mercy of Jill and Budge, who had the oars.

" *You'll* never row for your college," said Joan to Jill. Jill grinned.

" The question is—will *you* ? " she asked. " As a matter of fact I'm a poor hand with the oars, Commy," she said, turning to me, " but you'd be surprised to find what a good fisher I am. I've fished with my father a lot, and last time we were in Scotland I caught . . ."

" Sh ! Sh ! " said Budge, laying a hand over her mouth, " none of your angling yarns here, my child. Remember we're an honest crowd and you must restrain yourself."

" I won't," laughed Jill. " I caught a three-pound salmon," she finished triumphantly.

" And let it go ? " Joan asked innocently.

" No, landed it ! " said Jill. " And ate it," she concluded.

" *Re* fishing," said Budge, " I liked that story Ma told at Camp pow-wow last night about Peter and Andrew being made fishers of men."

" Yes ? " I said, inquiringly.

" Because you see," said Budge, pulling laboriously at her oar, " I think if people profess to be Christians they ought to do something for their keep, so to speak."

" Now whatever do you mean by that ? " I asked.

" Well," said Budge, " I think it's pretty poor when anybody just gets converted or whatever you like to call it, and then goes on her way rejoicing because she's

safe for heaven, and never caring what happens to everyone else."

"Ah! Budge! you're right," I said, quickly. "But
—have you actually known a Christian like that?"

"Yes! I have," said Budge, a little defiantly. "Not
many, Commy, but I really have met them. There are
some in our church, I can tell you. They're at every
meeting that's ever held, but it seems to me it ends there."

"Now, Budge, I'm going to pin you down," I said.
"Give me an actual instance of what you mean, because
this is a very serious accusation that you have made."

The girl's face flushed.

"I'll give you two if you like," she said. "They've
just flashed into my mind. One of my aunts makes no
end of a noise about being a Christian, and when I was
staying with her last year she was always talking at
me. But while I was there, in one week this happened.
There was a class of twenty poor kids in the Sunday
School, and their teacher fell ill. The superintendent
came to auntie and simply begged her to take it for a
couple of weeks. He said they were terribly short-
staffed and all the classes were too big and he had tried
everybody he could think of. Do you think she would?
Not she! I was in the garden and I heard her talking
to him in the dining-room. She said, ' You know how
I would *love* to help, but I'm *so* busy, and in any case
I have a young niece here who keeps me very occu-
pied. . . .' My word, Commy, I felt mad! She does
nothing but sleep every afternoon, Sunday included,
and never turns her hand to a thing. As for my being
there preventing her . . ." Budge became speechless
for a moment. Then she continued :

"I'll tell you another thing that happened. She had
a little maid who really worked jolly hard, I thought.
She was a member of the Girls' Bible Class at the church
—that was how auntie got her. One evening, soon after
I was leaving, there was to be a big missionary meeting,
and this kid had a special invitation to go. She was

awfully keen on mission work, so she asked auntie if she might go from eight till ten. Auntie just smiled sweetly and said, ' I should have been *so* pleased to have let you, Alice, but we cannot leave the house, and I fear I ought to be present. People would think it so strange if I were not.' I almost offered to stay on and keep the house that night, but I don't think auntie would have let me."

There was silence. I think we all felt speechless.

" There's another thing comes to my mind," said Budge, " which shows that it isn't only the well-off Christians who act like this. One of my other aunts has three children and one maid, and this maid is a member of a church and spends all her off time (she has plenty of it) at her meetings. Well, last year, all the three children got measles and auntie couldn't afford to get a nurse so she had to manage herself, and she nursed them night and day for three weeks and was worn to a shadow. The maid hardly did a thing extra, though she knew auntie simply hadn't a moment to do the dusting and the things she usually did. Then, at the end of three weeks auntie suddenly collapsed one morning and had to lie down with a desperate headache. It was the girl's afternoon off, and believe me, that girl went up to her at one o'clock and said : ' Will it be all right if I go before lunch instead of after to-day, Madam ? I'd have offered to change my half-day as you're so poorly, only we've a tea meeting on at the church and I'm arranging the cakes, so I'll have to go.' Auntie was almost too ill to reply, and the girl went out and stayed out till nearly midnight ; and unless a friend of auntie's had called unexpectedly that afternoon and seen to the children, I don't know what would have happened. And it's *that* sort of thing," Budge concluded in a hard voice, " that keeps me off religion."

" Budge ! " I could hardly speak for the shame which I felt. " That's not quite accurate. It's that sort of thing that you are allowing to be an *excuse* to keep you

' off religion ' as you say. But it's only an excuse. We
invite you to follow Christ—not to follow these selfish
Christians, and, my dear, you will never find *one* of these
things in Him. He was for ever at the service of others
—always helping, seeking, healing and loving people.
And His ideal and what He was for ever putting before
His followers was that they should do likewise—that
they should spend and be spent in winning others and
helping others."

The boat pulled slowly on, but nobody spoke. Over
the shining surface of the waters the gulls dipped and
rose. From far ahead the laughing voices of the girls
in the other boat came wafting back. The sun shone
—the world around gleamed and glinted with light. The
birds sang joyously from the cliffs nearby, but for the
first time in all that happy week, our hearts were sad.

" Now let's talk this out," I said at last. " It has
been hard hearing—what Budge has just told us—but
perhaps we were meant to hear it. For I expect we have
none of us been quite blameless. I expect we've all been
selfish and thoughtless at times, not realising what a
terrible stumbling-block these things may be to others.

" You know what Ma was saying last night about
our being commissioned by our Lord to be ' fishers '
for Him ? Well—I expect that we've all got to take
that more seriously in future. We're apt to think that
that sort of message is for missionaries and clergymen
and deaconesses and not just for the rank and file of us.
Whereas these men to whom the words were first said,
were the rank and file—just ordinary workers, as we are,
and the Lord came to them and said to them, ' Now in
future you've got to make *the main business of your life*
to win people to Me.' "

" You mean by our lives and witness, Commy ? "
said Joan.

" Yes ! At this stage and throughout life for a great
many people, that is the way to win others. ' *By their
fruits ye shall know them.*' And this method *does* win

B

people. Budge, I've let you have your say this afternoon," I said, turning to her ; "now just listen while I tell you this simple, true story.

" I used to help in a working girls' club and the leader of that club was the most Christlike woman I have ever known. She was full of fun, and she had a keen sense of humour, as indeed she would need to have for such work as she did.

" One year I went to camp with these girls. I was talking to one of them—a rough, working girl, whom I greatly admired and who was a most sincere Christian. She had recently been made a worker among the juniors in the club and they all thought the world of her. I knew something of that girl's past life—of her home and parentage—and suddenly I wondered what had led to this great change. I said to her :

" ' Laura, what first led you to seek Christ ? '

" She jerked a thumb over in the direction where the club leader was standing. ' Her ! ' she said, briefly.

" I needed no further explanation. Knowing the woman, I understood. It was not her preaching, but her life. She was human, but she was also Christlike, and in her words and actions she was like Him. Oh ! my dears, if only we were all like that ! If only every girl who professes to love and follow Him were *like* Him. Then we should all be fishers."

We didn't talk much more—we had to pull in soon after that, for it was nearly tea-time. But that night, after prayers, Trim gripped my arm. Now Trim was not an emotional person, so I was a little surprised to find that her eyes were full of tears.

" Commy ! " she said. " That talk in the boat this afternoon ; it's made all the difference to me. I've been a Christian for years, but I've never been a real fisher. I've never made it the business of my life. I must have been a hindrance to heaps of girls. But I've asked Him to forgive me . . . and . . . bless me . . . and . . . help me to be a whole-time worker for Him now."

VI. GOOD OR BEAUTIFUL ?

We had all had an exhausting afternoon in Camp. There had been an inter-Camp hockey match and we had played to the death in spite of a scorching sun. The sides had been chosen—*Brains* v. *Beauty*—and Beauty had won. " It always does," said Trim, mournfully stroking her large nose.

Now it was nearly tea-time and we were all stretched out on the lawn, waiting for tea to come out. A quick bathe had done much to refresh us, but none of us felt inclined to move.

I was still feeling a little sore at having been unanimously voted on the side of Brains. It was strange how eager we all were to be on the side of Beauty. Yet, as Joan remarked, " Brains are so awfully useful." There were shrieks of laughter as each girl was voted to one side or the other. Ma, much to my chagrin, was allocated to Beauty.

" Why ! she's *ten* years older than I am," I protested.

" Ah ! Commy ! There are some whom age cannot wither," Jill giggled. " You're evidently not one of them, but Ma is ! "

The game, as it turned out, was very well matched, but, as I said, Brains lost. " We played under a handicap," said Trim. " There is a psychological effect in knowing you are beautiful ; or perhaps I should say in *thinking* you are," she corrected.

" Sour grapes ! " laughed Budge, who had been a Beauty.

" No," said Trim, " not at all ! But yes—perhaps just a little," she grinned. " I'm quite sure that all you Beauties had a sense of superiority this afternoon that made you play better. Not that you ought to have had it," she added, " for when all's said and done there wasn't much to choose from on either side."

A howl of laughter greeted her remark. When it had subsided, someone asked :

" Commy, would you rather be good or beautiful ? "

" Well, as you won't hold out any hopes about being beautiful, I suppose I've got to be good," I retorted.

" No, but seriously, which would you like to be ? "

" Both ! " I returned promptly.

" Commy ! answer a plain question," said Budge, rolling over and fixing me.

" Why should I ? " I asked. " Why should I expose my inmost soul to twenty hungry girls sprawling on a lawn ? "

" Because there's ten minutes before tea and we've nothing to do," said Jill. " Do tell us which you'd honestly rather be, Commy."

" Good," I said.

" *Really !* "

" Truly ! "

" But why ? " came in a chorus from a little group of girls.

" Because I'd have a better time," I said.

Budge sat up. Her eyes opened like saucers, and she said :

" *Have a better time!* But, Commy, you don't have *nearly* such a gay time if you're good."

" I didn't say ' *gay*.' I said ' *better*,' " I replied. " I've seen old people who've led a gay life and I've seen old people who've led a good life, and I know which I'd rather be."

" Well, I don't agree with you," said Budge, hastily. " I think it's all right to be good up to a point, but I don't agree with Christians not going in for dancing and smoking and cinemas and all that sort of thing. It makes life so dull. Personally, I don't think there's any harm in anything so long as it doesn't hurt you or anyone else."

I couldn't help smiling at Budge's vehemence. She was always so very sure and so very provocative.

"Now look here, Budge," I said. "You're trying to lead me into a first-class argument, and I'm not going to be led. For one thing because I'm too hot, and for another because it wouldn't do any good. But if you really want to know what I think about this question of the Christian girl going in for these things I'll tell you . . ."

There was silence, which I took for consent. Several girls had moved up from the outskirts of the group to listen.

"The first and obvious thing is that if we try to do both—live for Christ *and* live for the world—the one crowds out the other. There simply isn't *room* for both. Each is a whole-time job. You may not realise that just now while school takes up so much of your time, but just wait till you've left school. If you're a Christian your work for Christ will take up your thought and your time. If not, your social engagements will fill every minute of your all-too-short evenings. Even your thoughts during the day will fly to what you are going to do at night.

"Now I'll tell you," I said, "what made me give up the attempt to make God and the world fit in together in my life. For quite a while after I came to Christ I went on in the way I'd been accustomed to. I didn't 'grow' a bit in my Christian life, and sometimes I used to wonder why. I never had any real love for the Bible. I liked going to meetings, but the effect of them used to wear off pretty quickly. Then, one winter, there was a big run of dances in the town. One night after another they came, during the weeks after Christmas. I couldn't accept one and refuse another—it would have caused offence. Night after night I reached home in the early hours of the morning, and do you think I could pray? Of course I couldn't! I was too tired mentally and physically. I had to sleep on till the last minute in the mornings. There was certainly no time for prayers and reading then. After the first week I thought I'd

have a rest after lunch on Sunday before going to my
class. I went dead asleep and woke, much refreshed,
as the tea gong went ! The next Sunday I was tired
again, so I decided to sleep the afternoon out again.
The following week I met the leader of my Sunday class
in the High Street. We stopped and spoke, and I
explained rather shamefacedly why I had not been to
class. She said :

" ' Do you belong to Christ, or to the world ? '

" I said, ' Why ! I belong to Christ now—you know
I do.'

" ' Then,' she said, ' you cannot serve two masters.
For either you will hate the one and love the other or
else you will hold to the one and despise the other. You
cannot serve God and Mammon.'

" That was the end of it for me. I went home, and
on my knees I asked God for grace to cut out of my life
every thing which hindered, even though it might not in
itself be wrong. From that moment I began to ' grow
in grace ' and to know a happiness which I had certainly
not known before. I got thrilled with the class and my
job in it. These Camps are one outcome of it."

I paused. A girl, who had hitherto seemed unin-
terested, said :

" Go, on Commy ! "

" The other thing," I said, " is that if you try to live
for God and the world, your love for God will take the
snap out of your wordly pleasures. What I mean is,
that a Christian never *wholly* enjoys being wordly. There
is just enough godliness in her to make her recoil from
much that happens. There are just one or two things
in the otherwise enjoyable ' show ' which make her soul
shrink, if it is attuned to God. She cannot laugh naturally
at all that happens. She cannot view sin, as it is so lightly
depicted nowadays, without a shudder, because, you see,
she knows it nailed her Saviour to the Cross."

There was silence for a few moments as I finished
speaking. Overhead the gulls swooped and circled.

Away in the distance the waves sucked gently at the shore, and the murmur of them came up to us as we sat on the lawn. Jill broke the silence.

"Then, Commy, what are the things you think are wrong for a Christian, or perhaps I should say 'harmful'?"

I thought for a moment and then said:

"That question, Jill, I am not going to answer. I couldn't go into it with this audience without getting into very deep waters. Because, you see, all that is harmful for me may not be for you. To explain what I mean. I once heard of a Christian man who had to give up playing chess for the simple reason that he became so good at it that it obsessed him. When he tried to pray at night, he was thinking out moves. I knew personally a girl who found exactly the same about tennis. All the time she was trying to get a contact with God she was thinking out strokes, so she gave up playing till the fever left her, and then she found herself able to take it up again.

"Now, nobody in their senses would say there was anything wrong in chess or tennis," I said. "It just happened that for two people they spoiled their communion with God. And I'm not going to say what will spoil yours. All I would say is this : if you want to be the very best for God, ask Him to show you what will hinder that. He will do it. There is nothing He wants more for His child than that she shall be wholly His, and therefore wholly happy. There is a verse in John vii which says : '*If any man will do His Will, he shall know of the doctrine.*' If we follow Him step by step, if we ask *His* counsel about what will help and what will hinder, we shall know, for He will tell us."

The gong clanged through the house and it was followed by Ma heading a procession bringing out the tea.

"I'm so sorry tea is late," she said.

"I'm not," said Jill.

ONE morning during the last week of Camp I woke at six o'clock instead of seven. I think it may have been due to a young thrush, who had flown into my bedroom, helped himself to a nice, if meatless, breakfast out of a biscuit tin left open on the window sill, and was proceeding, as a grateful little thrush should, to sing his grace before departing.

He sang loud and long. Such an unexpected feast demanded an extra pæan of praise and gratitude. In the middle of it I woke—he gave a final, rather startled, trill, and disappeared.

It was such a lovely morning. It seemed a waste of time to go to sleep again, so I decided to go for an early morning walk. Ma was snoring comfortably on the other side of the wall, and I decided not to waken her, but just to get off on my own. There was time, if I went quickly, to reach the Cader Gorge and get back for breakfast.

Out in the garden the air was intoxicating. It simply made one want to dance for joy. I sped over the lawn, and out at the west gate. From there it was a good half-hour to the Cader Gorge, mostly through cornfields.

But as it happened I was never to reach the Cader Gorge that morning. For as I passed through one cornfield and was just reaching the second, I heard, from the other side of the hedge, the sound of singing. They were girls' voices, fresh and clear as the morning itself, and these were the words that floated to me :

> " *The early morn with Jesus—His happy welcome guest.*
> *The first glad thoughts for Jesus, the brightest and the best.*
> *Alone, alone with Jesus, no other may intrude.*
> *The secret of Jehovah is told in solitude.*"

I peeped over the hedge, and there, with their Bibles on their laps, sat Joan and Jill.

Perhaps it was the snapping of a twig by my leaning on it that made them turn round and see me. They stopped singing and Joan said :

" Why, Commy, how *marvellous !* Fancy meeting you ! Do you often do this ? "

" No ! I don't ! " I said. " I woke up early by mistake this morning. But do *you ?* " I asked.

" Yes !—well, at least, we've been out several mornings," Joan said. " We're certainly earlier than usual this morning. We were so early and it was so lovely, that we got to singing. Come and sit down, if you're not doing anything special."

" I'm not ! " I said, giving up all idea of the Cader Gorge. " This is a lovely spot you've found."

" Yes ! we've had some grand times here," said Jill. " I can't tell you what a thrill these Q.T.'s have been for me, Commy. I always used to gabble a prayer through in the mornings at home—at least, I did when I remembered, but I've never known what it is to have a real Quiet Time in my life."

" Well, Jill, I'm glad you've found the joy of it so soon," I said, as I sat down, " because it's going to be one of the most important things when you get home."

" Yes, Joan says that," Jill answered. " Of course— I suppose," she said, a little wistfully, " it won't be quite the same thrill as here, in Camp."

" I know what you mean," I said. " And certainly there is a ' thrill ' about everything in Camp that we can't carry with us to our homes. But you know, Jill, we can't live on ' thrill '—it is altogether too exciting. We must live on the real things which in this case are behind the thrill. And even if our Q.T.'s are less thrilling in a cold bedroom on a raw November morning, they can be, and will become, increasingly dear and necessary to us. I don't mind giving you two a very personal illustration to explain what I mean,' I laughed.

" When I first got engaged it was mid-summer, and every time my fiancé and I arranged to meet the sun was

glowing and the world was beautiful. How I longed
for those meetings ! Then later the winter came, and
instead of meeting in an orchard, which had been our
favourite spot, we met at the British Museum—cold to
the feet and improving to the mind. But do you think
I looked forward any the less to those meetings ? Not
I ! My hand fairly shook with excitement as I buttoned
up my stormproof coat to go out. Because, you see,
each time I was getting to know him better and love
him more and each time I wanted more and more to be
with him. So that after a time the *place* didn't really
matter. It was meeting *him*.

"There is a priceless picture hanging in our hall at
home," I continued. "I used to think it hopelessly
idiotic, but now I understand it. It's a picture of the
dreariest, wettest, most miserable of all winter days,
in a London park. You can positively *feel* the fog and
the damp. Over a sodden pavement a young man and
woman are walking. They look so happy. The picture
is titled, ' The Garden of Eden.' "

"That's rather nice," said Joan, thoughtfully.

"Yes, it is," I agreed, " and ever since I've been a
Christian I've thought it is a very true illustration of the
Christian life, and especially of communion with our
Lord. For as we get to know Him better, *any* time
spent with Him—it doesn't matter where—becomes
wonderful and precious. And the more time we spend
with Him alone, the more time we want to spend."

"Joan says it is the first thing that the devil will try
and put an end to," said Jill.

"Joan is right," I said. " Our enemy knows only
too well what strength for the day comes from those
moments at the beginning of it."

"So he will try to make us forget it ? "

"Or else put some good excuse in the way of our
neglecting it ' just for once.' At any rate, Jill, he will
use all his wiles to get it cut out of your life. Now, as a
matter of fact," I said, " I'm glad you raised that question

of the ' thrill ' of it, because I've known girls who have
gone home from a Camp like this full of enthusiasm, and
full of determination to keep sacred the morning tryst
which has meant so much to them at Camp. Then, as
you say, they have not found the same thrill in having
it by themselves at home, and bit by bit they have dropped
it, and the devil has had his way.

" Now the thing those girls had never realised is that
both prayer and Bible study are an *effort* to begin with.
Later—as I have said—when we begin to know Him—
it becomes pure joy, and we are filled with the longing
not to miss these special sacred times of communion.
But I believe that in the life of every very young Christian
there is at first the struggle to continue this habit. Once
we have definitely made it an unbreakable habit it will
not be nearly so easy for the enemy to trip us up, because,
you see, good habits *grow*, as well as bad ones."

I noticed that Joan's face was a little downcast as I
was talking. She looked up when I stopped, and said :

" That's awfully true about it being an effort at first,
Commy. I hadn't quite realised that it meant so much
persistence on our part. I think a lot of us feel that
it's only worth praying when we feel in the mood for
it."

" Ah ! now that's just what I'm getting at, Joan,"
I said. " You've put into words what I was thinking.
Prayer and Bible reading must never wait for moods
but must be a regular habit, with or without moods. A
soldier in battle doesn't wait till he feels in the mood for
it to go and take his orders from his captain. He receives
them every morning—regularly. And you and I are
soldiers in a great battle—the battle of life. So we've
got to get our orders from the Captain every morning,
and to report every evening, moods or no moods."

" I'm glad to know that," said Jill. " I think I'll
remember when I'm tempted to cut my Q.T. morning
or evening."

" I think I can help you," I said. " I'm going to

give you a prayer adapted from one of Charles Spurgeon's hymns. Stick it in your Bible, Jill, and read it when the enemy tries to make you neglect your Lord's tryst."

I passed these words over to her :—

Sweetly the holy hymn breaks on the morning air ;
Before the world with smoke is dim I come to Thee in prayer.
While flowers are wet with dew, Dew of my soul descend ;
Ere yet the sun the day renews, O Lord, Thy Spirit send.

Upon the battlefield before the fight begins ;
I seek, O Lord, Thy sheltering shield to guard me from my sins.
Ere yet my vessel sails upon the stream of day
I plead, O Lord, for heavenly gales to speed me on my way.

On the lone mountain-side before the morning's light.
The Man of Sorrows wept and cried and rose, refreshed with might.
Oh ! hear me then, for I am very weak and frail ;
I make the Saviour's Name my plea, and surely must prevail.

Just before supper on that last evening of Camp a group of girls ran up to me and asked :

"Commy, can we have a proper pow-wow to-night round a camp fire? We could have it in the copse, and we'd go down and get the fire going if you agree?"

"Why, that would be marvellous," I said. "Any of you Guides?"

"Yes! Rather!" replied Jill. "There are six of us with our camper's badge. We'll do it. And Trim will be useful to stand on the windward side as a screen," she added roguishly.

"And Jill," said Trim solemnly, "should have plenty of breath to fan the flames."

"There you are, Jill," laughed Joan. "Put that on your needles and knit it, you young chatterbox. Trim had the last word that time. All right, Commy, we'll get going and have a roaring fire by supper time."

I thought, as we filed into the house, that I had never seen a much more unhappy girl than Budge. I did what I had never done before—drew her aside as we passed the officers' room.

"Budge," I said, "are you coming to the pow-wow to-night?"

The girl turned a hard face towards me.

"Is it compulsory, Commy?" she asked.

"No! it isn't. You know it never is."

"Then," she said, "I'd rather not come."

The girls kept their word. When we trooped down to the copse an hour later a cheery, crackling fire greeted us, and we were soon sitting in a ring round it singing choruses.

When the last favourite had been chosen, I said :

"Now let's have a pow-wow. Any questions you like, only first let me tell you a story."

The girls settled themselves comfortably and I began.
" There was once a little group of perplexed men
sitting together in a house in Jerusalem. There had
been a time when they were full of hope and enthusiasm.
They had given up everything in order to follow a Leader,
whom they had loved and trusted. They had looked
forward to his being made a king, when they would
share his glory with him. And what had happened . . . ? "

I paused. Someone answered in rather a hushed voice.

" The Leader had been crucified, Commy."

" Yes ! You've recognised the story. And after He
was crucified He was buried, but after three days He rose
from the grave and those followers of His saw Him again."

" They must have been frightfully bucked at that,
Commy."

" Yes, I think they were. But you see, after another
forty days He went away again—in the most amazing
fashion. One moment He was standing talking to them
and the next He had been taken up . . . up . . . up
out of their sight. And I think they knew that this time
it was for good."

" So it was that which made them so perplexed ? "

" Yes—partly. But I think also it was the fact that
before He went their Leader had left them such a big
task. He had left them the job of telling the world about
Him. And I believe while He was with them they felt
they could do it. But once He had gone, they didn't."

" And why were they in the house in Jerusalem,
Commy ? "

" Because their Leader had told them that He would
send them the power to do this great task. And they
were waiting for that power."

" And what was that power, Commy ? " asked Jill.

" It was the Holy Ghost," I replied. " He came and
filled their hearts and lives, flooding them with light and
power. He made such different people of them that they
went out straightway from that house and before evening
had fallen three thousand souls had been brought to Christ."

" *Three Thousand !* " echoed Jill, incredulously.

" Yes," I said, " and do you know who brought them ? "

" No. Who ? " asked a camper.

" Why, Peter. The man who a few days before had shrunk away at the taunt of a maidservant and had denied that he ever knew his Lord. Directly the Holy Spirit filled him, he went out and preached Christ. He simply couldn't help it, you see. He was so full of it. And the Power within him was so great that those who heard came to Christ. They were compelled—because of the Power."

" Oh, Commy ! " The words came involuntarily as Jill leaned forward, the firelight playing on her face. " If only we could have that power, too."

" We can, Jill," I said. " Every girl who is truly a child of God—every one of us who has come to Him, through Jesus Christ—can know the same power as those disciples of old knew, because, you see, we already—now—have the Holy Spirit living within us."

There were puzzled faces looking at me in the firelight. I went on to explain.

" Whenever anybody comes to Christ, He puts His Holy Spirit within them. You didn't know that ? But listen ! ' After ye believed ye were sealed with the Holy Spirit.' So, you see, if you are the child of God you have His Holy Spirit dwelling within you. God sealed the transaction by giving you His Spirit."

" Then why can't we be like the disciples were ? Why haven't we their power, Commy ? "

" There are many to-day who have," I said, " and if we lack power it is because we don't give the Holy Spirit full sway in our lives. We put Him in the background, only listening to Him when we want to, instead of asking Him to take entire and full control of our lives."

" And if we let Him take control ? " Trim asked.

" Then," I said, " our lives would be flooded with power, and all the problems we have been talking about in Camp would be settled. Because, you see, the work

of the Holy Spirit is to glorify Christ—*in us.*   And as
that happens increasingly, so our difficulties melt away
and we are left free to serve our Lord."

"Go on, Commy ! " said Jill.

"Well, we've been talking about guidance and knowing we are going the right path," I said.   "Now our
Lord said of the Holy Ghost, ' *When He, the Spirit of
truth, is come, He will guide you into all truth.*' We've been
talking about knowing for certain and never doubting
that we belong to Christ.   ' The Spirit beareth witness
with our spirit that we are the sons of God.'   We've been
talking about how we may conquer our difficulties and be
real, living witnesses for our Lord.   Well, *Ye shall receive power,
after that the Holy Ghost is come upon you.*'   He is the dynamic,
the driving force behind the Christian's life.   The tragedy
is that so often He is not given scope to work."

"I never realised that before, Commy," said one of
the campers.   "I've often felt that I'd give anything
to be a really powerful sort of Christian, and all the time
I've had the power within me, but chained up, as it were."

"That's just it," I said.   "The power chained up.
When it is released, then things begin to happen."

"And how can it be released, Commy ? " asked Jill.

"In just the same way as you were released from the
burden of your sin, Jill.   When you came to Christ you did
two things : you asked and you believed. He did the rest."

"Go on, Commy," came a voice from the circle.

"Well, now, here we are, a little group of Christians
wanting power—longing to be used by our Lord.   We've
got the source of power within us—the Holy Ghost.
We've got the promise of our Lord, ' *Ask and ye shall
receive, that your joy may be full.*'   All that remains to be done
is the asking on our part—just as simple an asking as when
we asked our Lord to forgive our sins and make us His.

"And then," I continued, "we have got to trust
just as we trusted that He had heard us for forgiveness.
We have got to believe that He *has* filled us, even if we
don't have any different feeling, when it has happened."

"Shan't we feel different, though?" asked Trim.

"We may," I said. "There are many Christians who, the moment they trust Christ for the fullness of the Spirit, are filled and flooded with the joy of the Lord. But there are others who are not. I'll tell you, if you like, what was my own experience."

"Please do, Commy," said Jill.

"I remember well," I said, "seeing this truth very clearly one evening, after reading a book that had come into my hands. For some long time I had been dissatisfied—my Christian life was not joyful, and my work for the Lord (I was leading a Sunday class) seemed dry and unfruitful. I found it hard to prepare, and my words when I gave them seemed dry and lifeless.

"Then, as I say, this book came into my hands, and as I read it I realised that, as you've just said, a great power was chained up inside me. It had never been released simply because I had never asked that it should. So straightway I asked."

"And what did you feel like, Commy?" asked Joan.

"Just the same as I did before, Joan," I said. "I got up from my knees feeling not the slightest bit different from when I got down. The next day was the same and the next, and after a few days the devil came and tempted me by suggesting that nothing had happened after all, so my prayer could not have been answered."

"And what did you do?"

"I went on believing. I just trusted doggedly. I kept saying, 'He promised to do it, so He must have done it. Feelings don't matter. Faith does. I *do* believe.'"

"And then?"

"And then the answer came. It was nearly a week later. I was sitting down to prepare my talk for the class on Sunday, when suddenly there came into my soul a new, sweet sense of my Lord's presence. I remember leaving my books and kneeling down by my bed, and as I knelt, the consciousness of His presence increased, until, as I stayed there, my whole being seemed flooded with the glory of the Lord. It was the most real experience I have ever had."

There was silence for quite a few minutes after that, then Trim asked :

"And did it make a difference, Commy? I mean to you and your work."

"Oh yes, it did," I said. "It didn't make me perfect by any manner of means—you all know that—but it gave me a joy which I never had before and a knowledge that there was power ready for my work for God."

"And has the joy and the power ever gone, Commy?"

"Yes—often enough," I said sadly. "When sin has come in, the joy and the power have gone while it stayed. They can't live together, you see. But when the sin has been turned out, and I have again claimed His forgiveness and His Holy Spirit's fullness, the joy and the power have come back."

Joan looked up and her face was very earnest as she said :

"I think this is the secret that many of us have been wanting, Commy. Some of us in the High School have been longing to get hold of girls, but we haven't seemed to go about it the right way. I think I'll know how to, now."

"And I," said another, "know what to do about my temper."

"And I," said Trim, "have got the secret for living like a Christian at home."

"Perhaps I won't be so selfish now," murmured another.

"And I'll not be so lazy over my work," said another.

We sat for a bit over the fire, which was dying down. To-morrow Camp would be over and we should all be going back home. I looked round the circle of girls and realised with thankfulness that not one of them would be going alone because they were all His, and He had promised, '*I will never leave thee nor forsake thee.*' Budge was the only one who would go away unblessed and unhappy. Poor Budge !

IX. AND BUDGE CAME TOO

It was seven years later. My husband and I and our two small children were living in a little old cottage in the heart of the Sussex downs. It was a house of dreams, where, on summer days roses and honeysuckle climbed over the porch and clematis crept in at the windows.

At the time of writing, however, it was not summer, but winter, and instead of roses and honeysuckle and clematis, a bleak wind crept round the house. I was standing by the dining-room window wondering whether to walk the two miles into the village to shop, which would have done me good, or to 'phone, which would not, when the 'phone rang. A minute later the maid entered the room.

" A lady to speak to you, madam," she said, " but she didn't give any name."

I took up the receiver and said, " Hullo ! "

" Hullo ! " said a voice, vaguely familiar. " It's Jill Wentworth. Is that you, Commy ? "

I fairly gasped down the 'phone. Although we had corresponded quite frequently during the first year or so after Camp I hadn't seen or heard anything of Jill or her friends for nearly two years.

" My dear ! " I said. " How *marvellous* to hear you again. Where are you and what are you doing ? "

" I'm at Victoria station and I'm 'phoning you," was the answer, accompanied by just the same old merry chuckle. " Look here, Commy. We've just had the strangest reunion. Joan and I were taking a day off together, and we came to Victoria to see about getting a train out somewhere for a good walk. We'd no sooner got out of the Underground when we bumped straight into Trim, who was meeting Budge, whom she hadn't

seen for years. So we suddenly thought it would be the
most fearful spree to come down and see you—all four
of us—if, by any chance it's convenient at such short
notice."

" Why, yes, I'd simply *love* it ! " I cried through the
'phone. " Come down at *once* all of you. I'm absolutely
free for the rest of the day. When can I expect you all
to arrive ? "

" Well, there's no reasonable train for another hour,"
was the reply, " so we thought we would all have a spot
of lunch together here and then come straight on. We
shall be with you by three o'clock."

The three pips went, and Jill rang off. I went down
to the kitchen to give some amended orders for the evening meal, and then decided to walk the children to
the village, as I should not be able to have them in the
afternoon.

During the walk, while the little ones chattered, my
thoughts were back to the old Camp days, and I was
picturing again those girls with all their young enthusiasm
and earnestness. I was remembering some of the talks
we had had, and how eager they had been to learn more
of the Way of Life, and I fell to wondering if they would
be equally keen now.

I knew vaguely what had been the course of their
lives. Jill, I knew, had gone in for medicine. She had
been a clever girl and had shown promise of doing well.
She would make an excellent doctor, I thought, with
her quick sympathy and friendly personality. She would
be well on with her training now.

Joan had gone up to the university and after that I
had heard from her once—a happy, keen letter. She
was on the staff of a big girls' school.

Trim, to everyone's amazement had suddenly, on
leaving school, developed a literary strain. " A terribly
dull one, of course," one of the girls had explained when
writing to me. " She writes leading articles on thoroughly
dull subjects for the most appallingly stodgy papers.

Trim would, wouldn't she ? " I smiled when I remembered Trim.

About Budge I knew practically nothing. She had never written, and I fancy that after my last Camp she had drifted away from the others, though she seemed to have kept up an intermittent friendship with Trim.

My thoughts were brought back from the past by my four-year-old daughter's piping voice. We had reached the village and were passing the toy shop. Finding that I was in a reflective mood and did not respond as well as usual, she had organised a halt, and was holding a conversation with her small brother.

" Look at those *lovely* soldiers in the window, darling," she was saying. She was always very motherly towards him.

" Pop-pops ! " announced that young man. He always referred to soldiers as pop-pops.

The little girl lowered her voice and in a hushed voice said :

" I believe they're *Christian* soldiers, darling."

My attention was effectively caught.

" Why ? " I asked.

" 'Cos they look to me as if they're marching as to war," was the reply. " Mummy ! " she continued, " did I hear you telling Mary there would be visitors for tea ? "

" You did," I said.

The little girl looked up suspiciously.

" Does that mean we'll have nursery tea without you and Daddy ? " she asked.

" I'm afraid it does," I answered.

A big sigh escaped her.

" I *thought* it meant some complication," she said.

We did our shopping and returned home ; and well before three o'clock I was waiting at the station, feeling, I must confess, quite excited at the thought of seeing the girls again. When the train drew in, a door burst open, and almost before it had drawn to a standstill Jill was out on the platform, nearly wringing my hand off in her delight at meeting again. Joan was behind her,

quieter but none the less affectionate. Then came
Trim, looking very little different from the solemn-faced
girl of seven years ago, but with the added dignity of
horn-rimmed spectacles. And behind Trim came someone I did not recognise until, the first greetings over,
Trim said solemnly :

" This is Budge, Commy."

I caught my breath. Was it really Budge—this
highly-finished product before me ? I tried to connect
up the fresh-faced, bobbed-haired schoolgirl of my
memory with this rather supercilious-looking young
lady. Her face was entirely made-up. It seemed, as
I first looked at her that there was not a spot of it left
to nature. A tiny hat was perched precariously on a
head covered with masses of tight curls. And that hair !
Why, surely Budge had been a dark-haired girl. But
now I was faced with the blondest of all blondes. For a
moment I was staggered Then I pulled my wits together and said :

" Why, Budge, how nice to see you too ! "

Budge extended a scarlet-tipped hand.

" How do you do ? " she said, somewhat frigidly.

Trim came to the rescue.

" She's all right inside, Commy ! " she said. " It's
only that she's been permed and all that sort of thing."
Trim peered at me through her spectacles. " You look
awfully well, Commy. We're all longing to see the cottage
and the children."

A few minutes' drive brought us to the cottage. The
children had been waiting in the garden ever since I
left the house.

" Why, Commy, it's all *marvellous*," cried Jill. " What
a perfectly lovely place ! And those children ! "

The two little ones stood hand in hand, making a
lovely picture against the background of the old cottage.
Their cheeks were crimson with the glow of health and
their faces solemn with the solemnity of all small children
when they meet strangers.

They shook hands all round, and then I noticed my little girl's eyes fixed in staring wonderment on Budge. If Budge noticed it she didn't appear to mind. She seemed more at ease with the children than she had been all through the drive from the station. She talked easily and naturally with them, and all the time the little girl's eyes never left her face.

We all went indoors then, and I sent the children up to the nursery to play, while I gave my visitors an early cup of tea. Over it they became once more the school-girls of seven years previously—all except Budge, who maintained her somewhat aloof air towards us all.

I learned that Jill, in her last year at hospital, was practically engaged to a young doctor, and that they were thinking very seriously of going abroad for the first years of their married life. Joan was exceedingly happy in her school work, and had started a class on Sundays for the boarders. Trim did not talk much about herself, but from the little she said I felt sure that no word would ever fall from her pen that was dishonouring to her Lord. She was the same serene, happy Christian as of old.

Budge, apparently, was doing nothing in particular. Her people were, I knew, very well-to-do, and had decided there was no need for her to " do a job." For one moment she was the old Budge, as she said, with a twinkle in her eyes :

" I've had several proposals, Commy, but each time I've remembered the whooping-cough and the butcher and the fifty years of breakfasts, and the husband losing his stud. I feel sure I should have been married long before this if it hadn't have been for Ma's words that night."

After tea Budge said :

" Let's go and see those adorable kids again. They look perfect angels."

" Do they ? " I said. " Well—take it from me—they're not ! But do let's go up for half an hour. I always play with them after tea. Then while Nannie puts them to bed we'll have a good chin-wag round the fire till dinner-time. It's simply lovely having you all."

We made our way up to the nursery and I opened the door. What I saw made me gasp, although I was used to them. Their nurse had gone downstairs to wash up their tea things and during her absence they had spent the time with great profit to themselves.

The little girl was seated on a stool in front of her dressing-table mirror. Her head was covered with small, curly shavings procured in days past from the carpenter's shed across the lane. For one second I wondered how they had adhered so naturally and in such vast numbers. Then I saw ! The small brother, standing on a chair behind her, was busy dipping yet another shaving into a large pot of glue, and was just preparing to fix it when we entered. On top of the shavings was perched a tiny black doll's hat.

The little girl, having delegated the hair to her brother (and I must say I was amazed at the skill with which he had done it) was busy with her face. She sat with a scarlet crayon in her hand, adorning her already cherry-like lips. The effect, though unfinished, was quite startling.

A burst of laughter came from the girls behind me. I looked round. Jill and Joan were doubled up. A slow, broad grin was spreading over Trim's face, and Budge, unable to restrain herself, was chuckling audibly.

"You children ! " I cried. "How *could* you invent such a thing ? "

They did not reply to my obviously silly question. Instead the little girl turned a solemn face to Budge and said :

"How did you manage your eyebrows ? Scissors ? "

That finished it ! We all sat down and laughed until we were weak. I must say I admired Budge. She was so sporting over it. After a bit the children started laughing too. I gave instructions for the hair to be washed at bath time and we played with them until their nurse came back.

When we returned to the drawing-room again the curtains had been drawn, shutting out the wintry scene, and chairs had been pulled up round a blazing log fire. The lamp had not been lit, but the firelight played over the room, lighting up the old oak beams and quaint corner niches. We sat down, and Joan and Jill, in characteristic fashion, squatted on the floor. For a minute we were all silent, enjoying the comfort of the fire. Then Jill said :

" Life has been very good since that last Camp, Commy."

" Yes, very good indeed," I said. " At least, I've found it so."

" So have I," said Joan.

" And I," said Trim.

" I suppose I have too—in a way," said Budge, feeling, I fancy, that something was expected of her. " But of course," she added, " nothing comes up to expectations."

" Oh, *Budge*," I protested, " it goes far beyond them ! Why, I never *dreamed* I'd be so happy as I've been these seven years ! "

" Oh well !—but you're different," said Budge hastily.

" Why ? " I demanded.

She didn't answer, so I said :

" As a matter of fact, Budge, you're quite right. I *am* different, and I'll tell you why. I've got a loving Father in Heaven who looks after me, and I do certainly believe that things *are* different because of that. I remember once telling you that Christians had a better time than those who aren't. You didn't believe me then."

" I don't know that I do now," said Budge, with something of her old, defiant air.

" Don't you ? I'm not so sure of that, Budge. But look here, I'd like to tell you all an absolutely true story. You used to be fond of them. Let's pretend we're at Camp again.

" When I was in the sixth form at a big High School, there were six girls elected as senior prefects. They were a funny mixture in some ways, for three of them were so different from the other three.

" The three I liked were real jolly, sporting girls. They were all in the first eleven, and they were straightforward and generous and as popular as any girls I've ever known. They were full of fun and would do anything to help anybody. They made splendid prefects because the whole school liked them and would do what they said without a murmur.

" I remember trying to get hold of those girls to come to a Bible class I attended. They were awfully decent about it and they all came at some time or another. I remember that none of them really settled down to it, although two of them came quite a number of times. I remember, too, that the leader of the class had several talks with them. But if they were impressed they didn't show it. One of them told me she didn't believe in too much religion. And bit by bit they dropped off altogether. After we left school they never came at all.

" The second three prefects were really terribly dull. Two of them were cousins and they were not a bit liked. They seemed so prim and proper and they weren't a bit good at games. The third was the most ordinary person, with nothing outstanding about her. She wasn't particularly good at work and she wasn't particularly good at games. Very third-rate, I considered. And these three prefects gave me a good deal of concern, for they were all regular members of the Bible class and all professed to have taken the Lord Jesus as their Saviour. I *did* wish they could have been a bit more interesting !

" Well—that was all fifteen years ago. I kept up with most of them for a few years, as one does, and then we moved from the district and I lost sight of them. But strangely enough, last week I met one of our old mistresses who is still on the staff of the school, and she told me the latest news of everyone. Budge," I leaned forward and

looked at her, " would you like to hear the story of those
six girls ? "

Budge looked a bit startled.   " Why, yes, if you like ! "
she said.

" Well—I'll tell you first about the three attractive
girls," I said.

" One of them—she was very pretty—went on to the
stage.   She made quite a bit of a name for herself.   Once
I saw her name up in lights at Leicester Square.   She was
starring in some show there.   She married an actor—lived
with him a few months—left him, and is now a bitter, dis-
illusioned woman of only just over thirty, living by herself
in rooms and getting what small parts she can for a living.

" The second—she was the most sporting of all three
—when she left school went in for dancing.   As a result
of it—at some dance or other—she met a man with whom
evidently she fell very deeply in love, and he with her.
They got engaged.   Exactly a week before they were due
to be married that girl discovered that the man whom
she was going to marry—in a church—in seven days'
time, was already married to a girl who had been in
our form all the way up that High School.   It broke her
heart.   She collapsed mentally and physically, and is
now a nervous wreck.

" The third—she was my favourite—went into an
office as a secretary.   I saw quite a lot of her for a little
while after we left school.   I was working in an editorial
office near her, and she used to come round to see me
and we often had tea together.

" One day she told me she was going to get married.
I didn't like the sound of the man and told her so.   I
think it offended her, for she didn't come to see me much
after that.   She married him, and gave up her job, and
after a few months I lost sight of her.

" Last week I heard something that I can hardly
bear to repeat even now.   For I learned that a year
after her marriage to this man, who turned out to be
both cruel and unprincipled, this lovely girl, who had

been my close friend in old days, and whom I had loved
and admired, had, in the bitterness of her soul, taken
her own life."

There was silence in the old room. The flames leapt
and crackled. I was glad I had not lit the lamps. Those
girls had been my own familiar friends and I minded
intensely for all of them, and the telling of their life-
stories was not easy.

Jill slipped her hand into mine. " And what has
happened to the others—the three dull ones ? " she asked,
after a long pause.

" Yes ! Let me tell you three more stories," I said.
" The lives of three girls, who though much less gifted
and less popular, had the Lord Jesus Christ as their
Saviour and Friend.

" Well—the elder of the two cousins went in for
nursing. She was extraordinarily painstaking and conscientious, and she met and married the most amazingly
painstaking and conscientious young schoolmaster. They
were very happy and their happiness has been greatly
increased, I imagine, by the arrival of six children, and
I shouldn't be surprised if they are all as painstaking and
conscientious as their parents."

" Six ! What a handful ! " said Trim.

" I'm not at all sure they would be," I laughed.
" I can't imagine that girl's children being anything
but helpful and tidy. Anyhow—they live in a blissful
little world of their own, and she takes Mothers' Meetings
and he runs a Lads' Club and apparently they are quite
an asset to the life of their village.

" Her cousin—a year younger—is the resident Leader
of a big Club for girls in London. I am amazed to
hear what she has accomplished among those girls.
This old schoolmistress says the girls have an immense
respect and liking for her, and she, apparently, has made
the most charming flat for herself where she entertains
her friends. She has marvellous health—camps with the
girls—and generally finds life thoroughly enjoyable."

I paused again. Budge had dropped her head into her hands. It was Joan who at length asked :

" And the third girl, Commy ? "

" The third girl—well—the third girl thinks she is probably the happiest of the lot, for no one *could* be happier," I said. " For, my dears, here is the third girl, sitting with you to-night. I wish—oh ! *how* I wish—that I could give my heavenly Father proper thanks for all His goodness to me. I have deserved so little, and He has given me so much. Budge," I said, turning to her, " it *is* true. God *does* keep His own. I've proved it."

Budge raised a face, white in the firelight and wet with tears. Seven years had dropped away, and in the humble, wistful girl before me I saw the child I had known and prayed for in days gone past.

" Commy ! " she said in a husky voice. " I turned my back on Christ at Camp. He called me and I refused. I've never had a really happy moment since. Is it too late, or,"—her voice dropped to a whisper—" can I come now ? "

It was Trim who answered.

" It can't be too late, can it Commy, because He said, ' *Him that cometh to Me I will in no wise cast out.*' "

" Then," said Budge, " I'm coming."

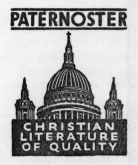

PATERNOSTER

CHRISTIAN
LITERATURE
OF QUALITY